DC
COMICS™

DC COMICS
COLOURING BOOK
★

STUDIO
PRESS
An Insight Editions Book

★ ★ ☆

From Superman and Wonder Woman's iconic reds and blues to the rich emerald hues of the Green Lantern Corps, vibrant colours are essential to bringing DC Comics' Super Hero stories to life on the page and screen.

Let the classic full-colour covers and art from DC Comics featured at the end of this book serve as a guide and inspiration for creating your own exciting adventures with your favourite characters.

★ ★ ☆

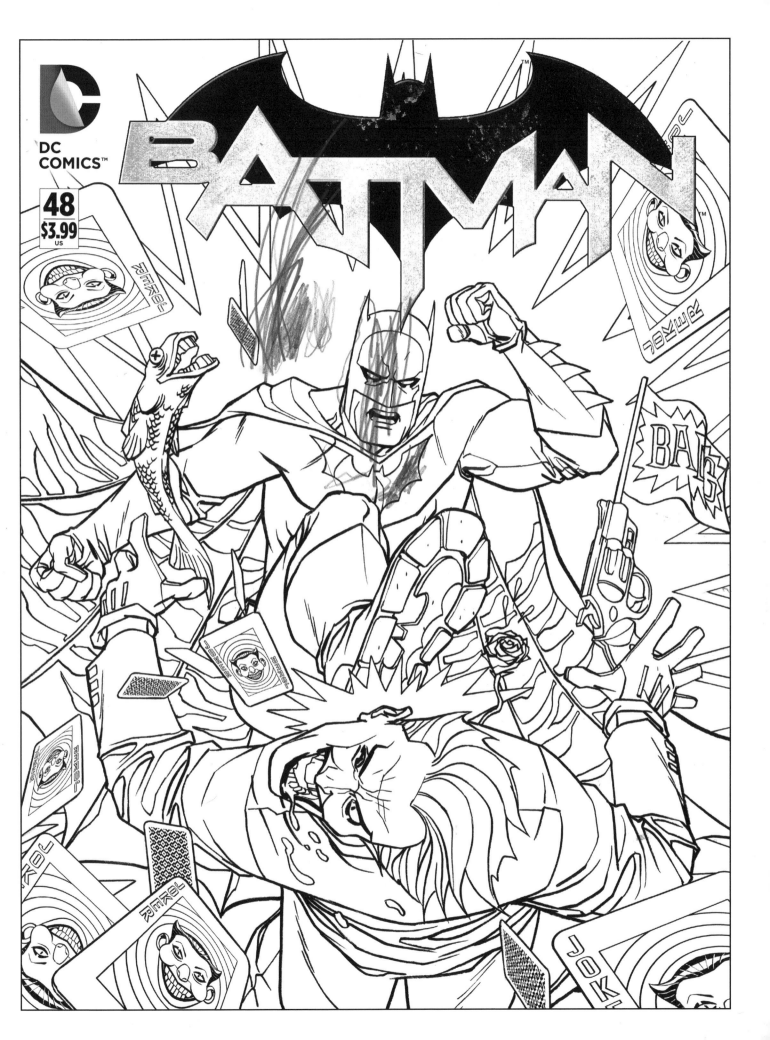

JUSTICE LEAGUE™

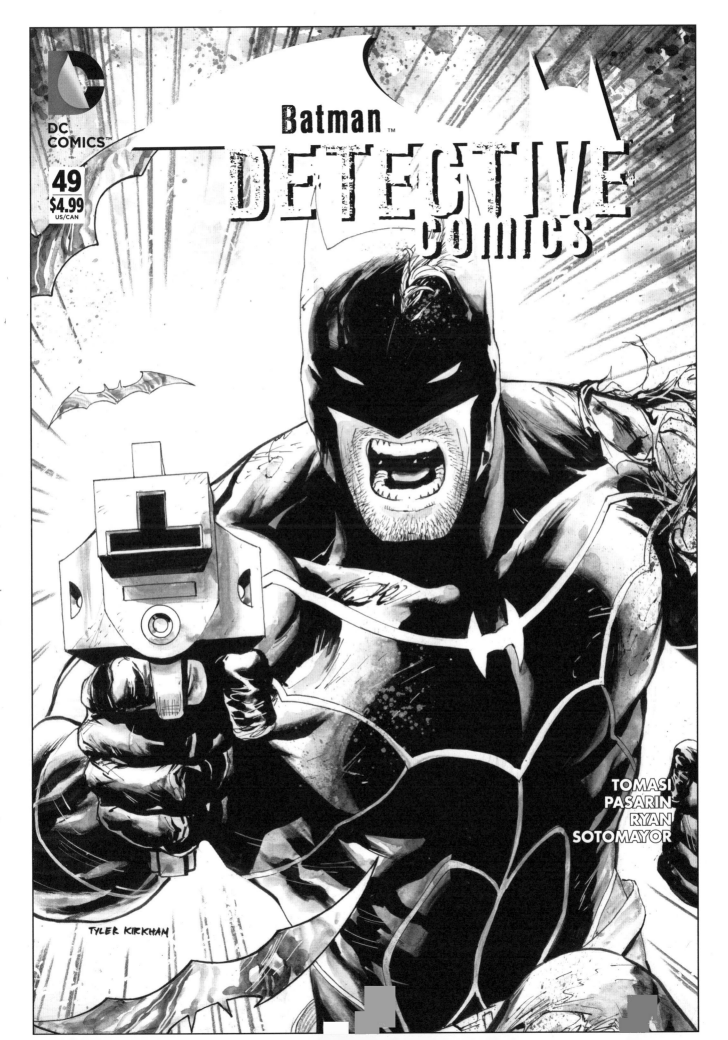

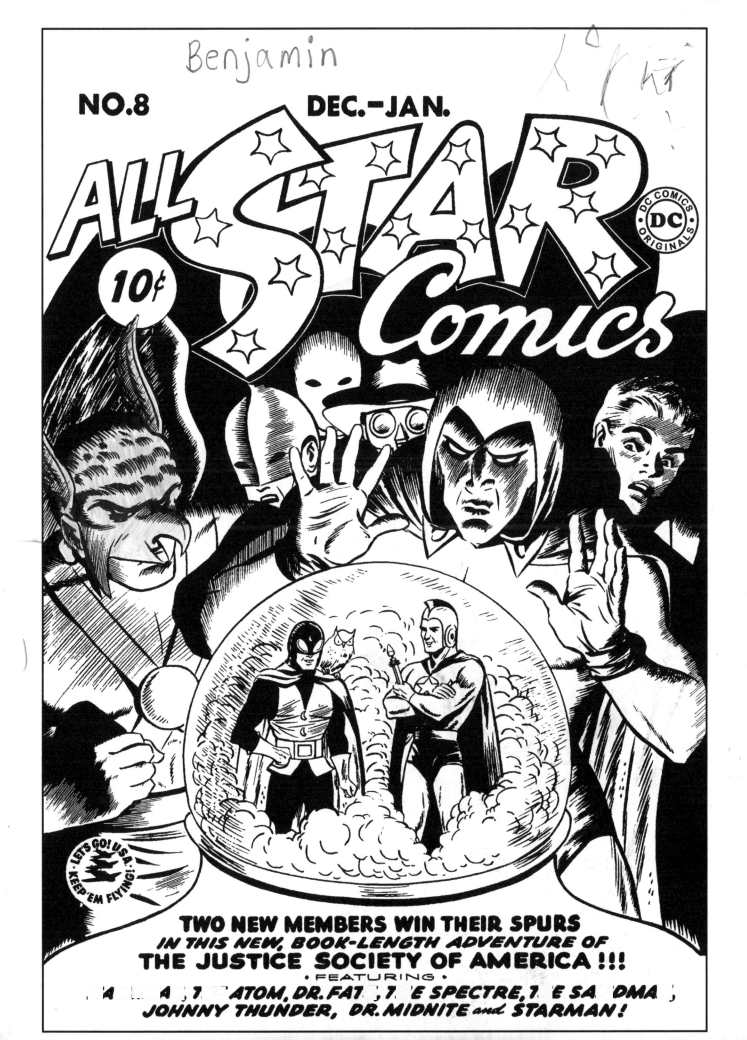

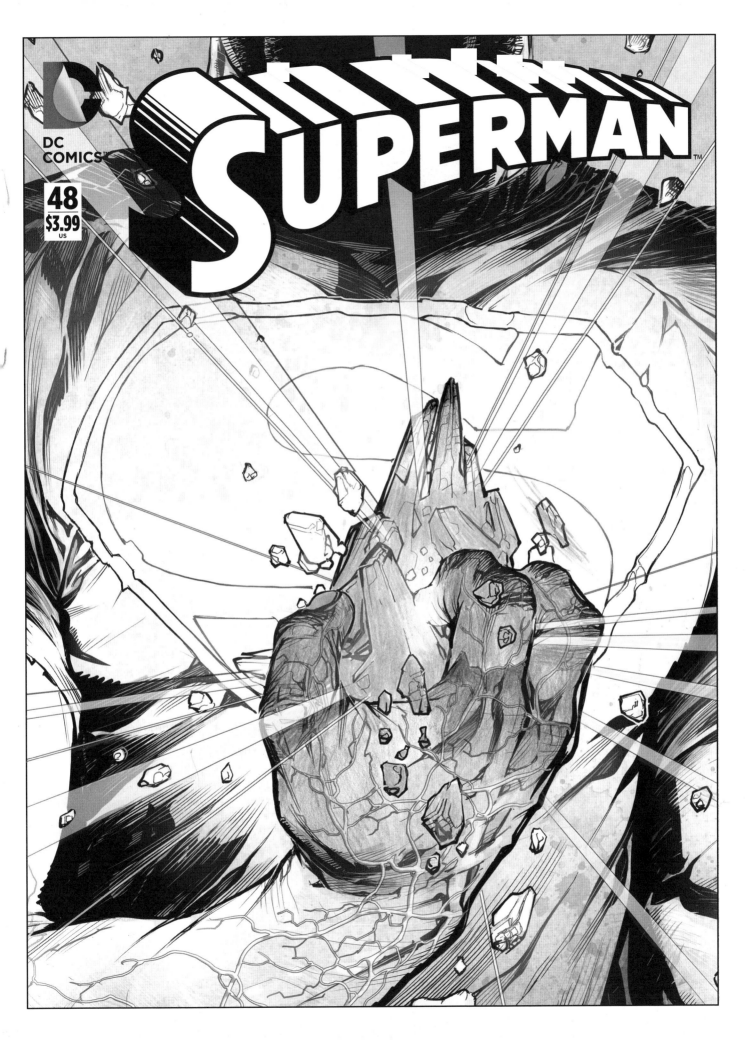

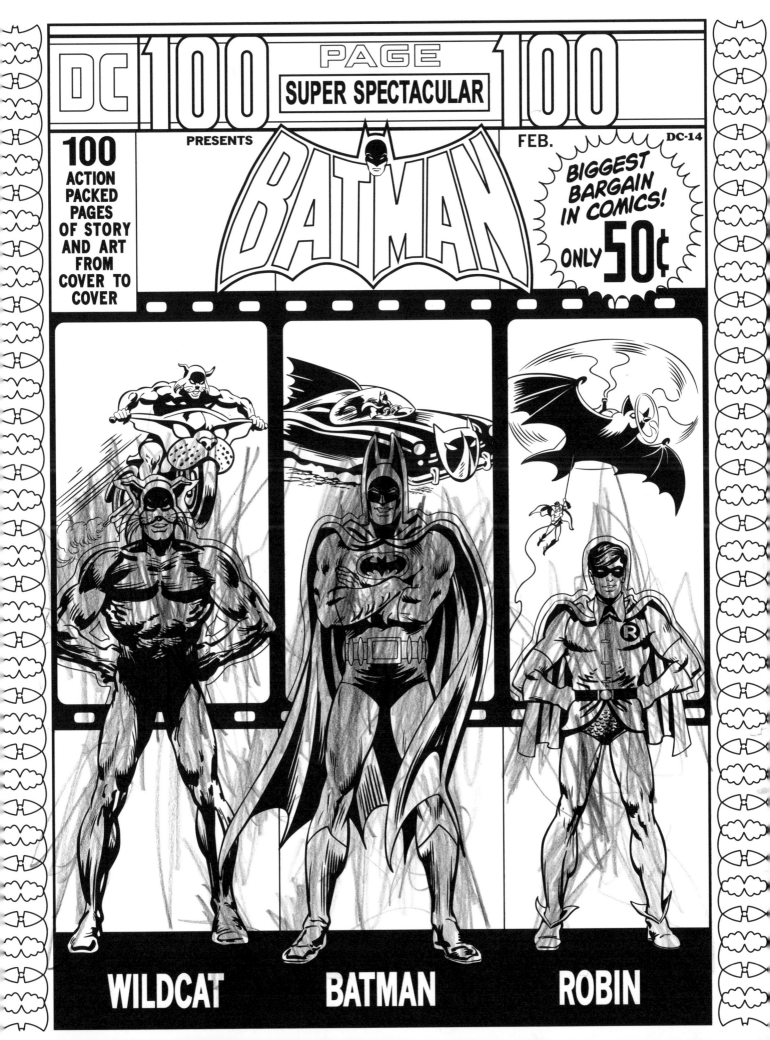

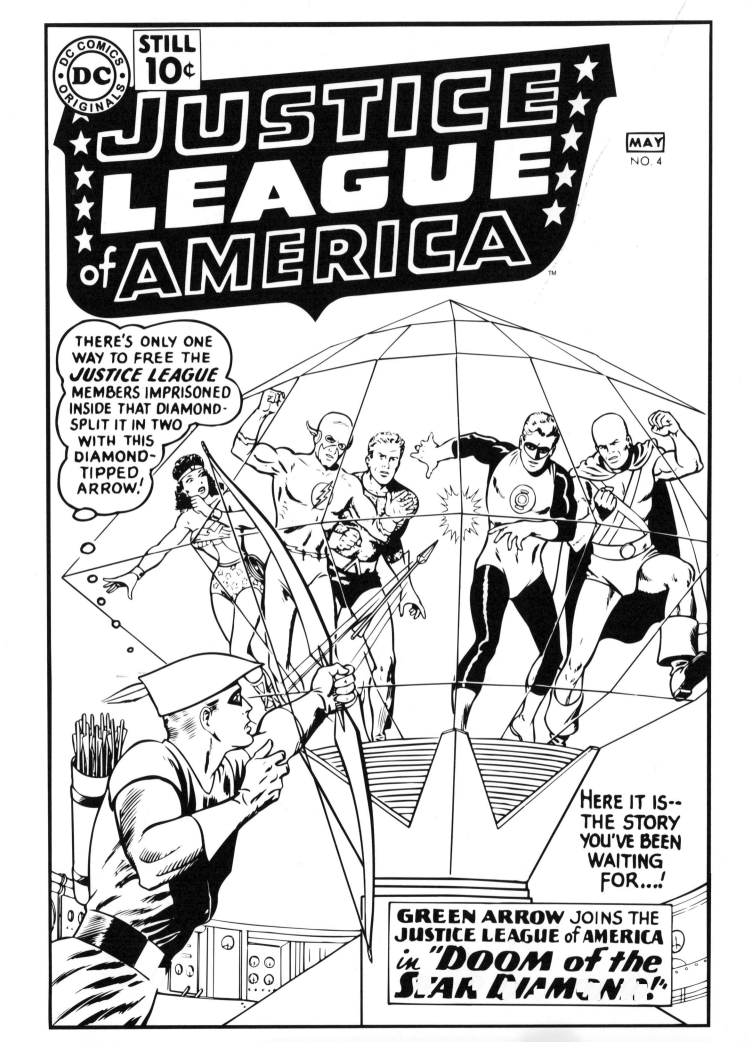

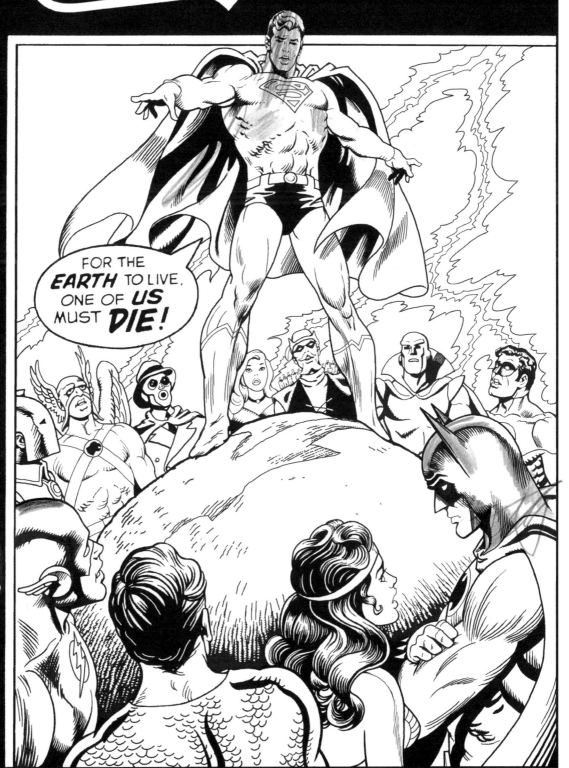

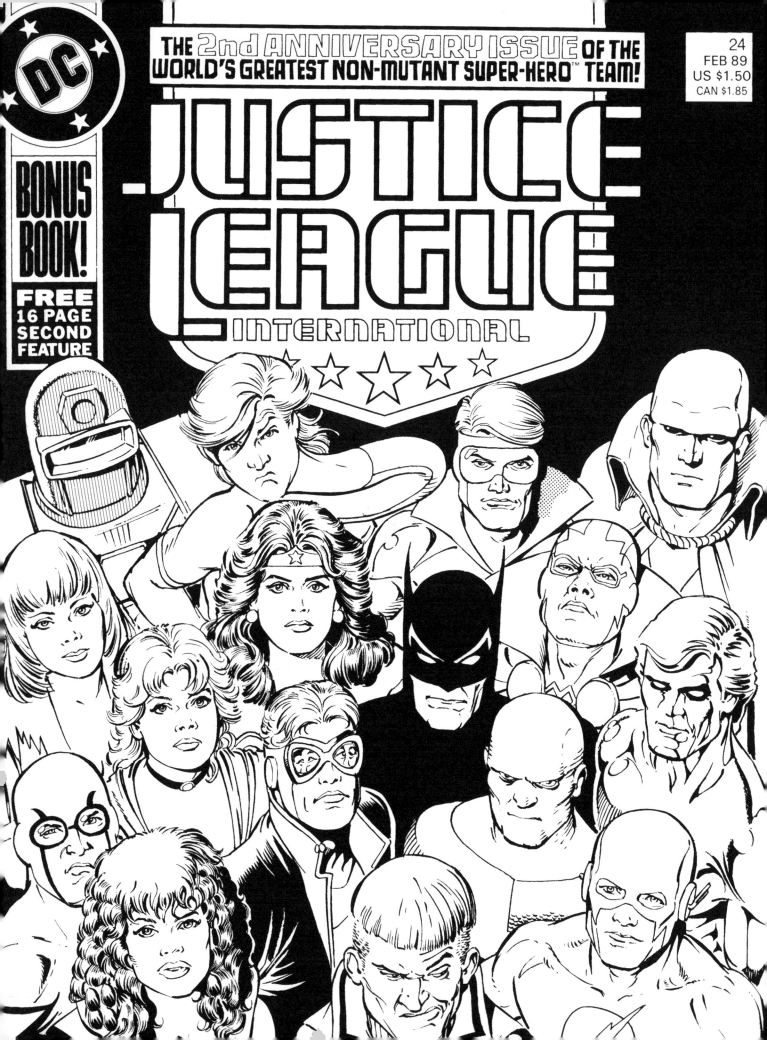

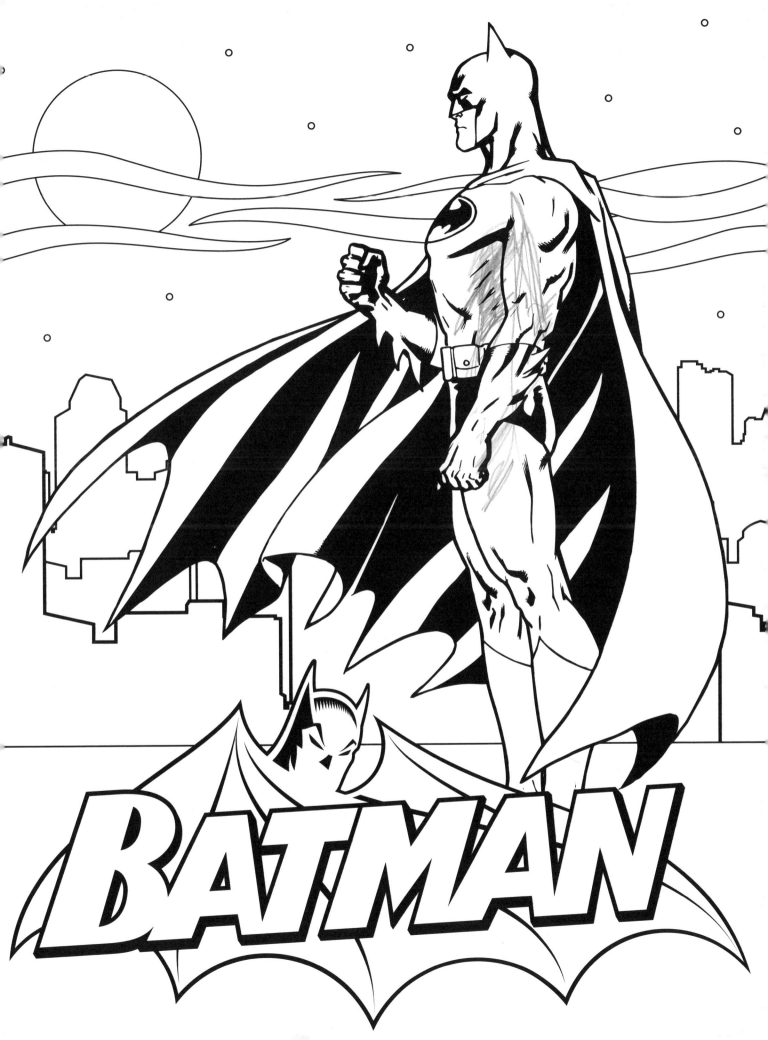

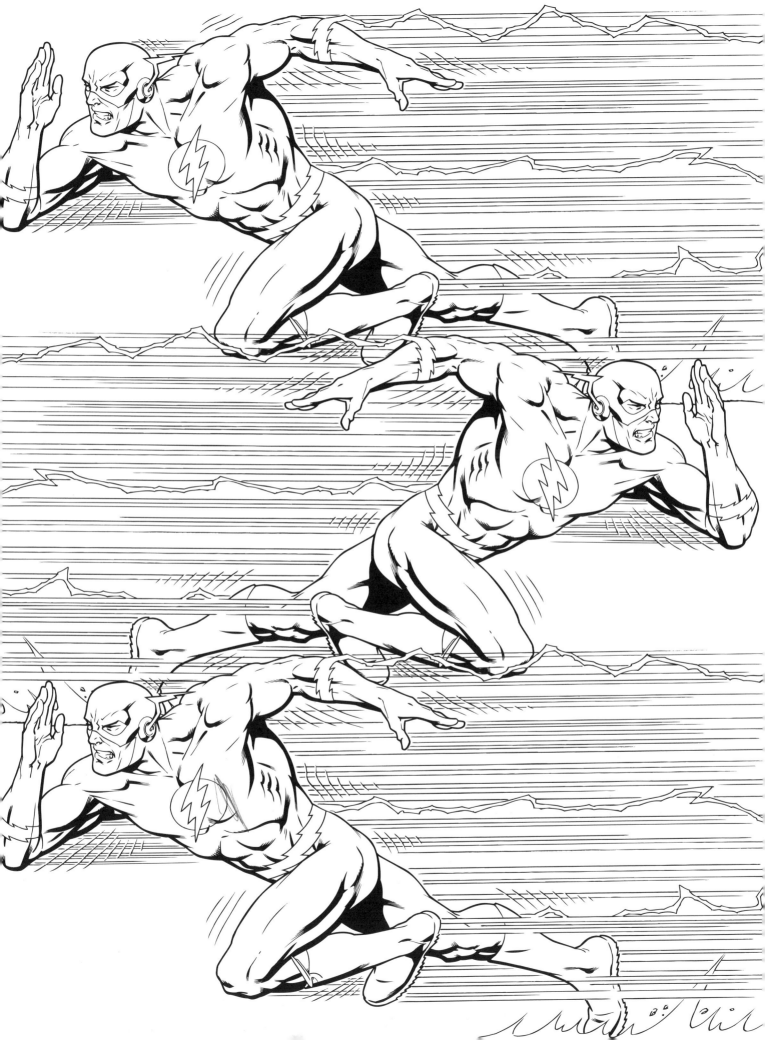

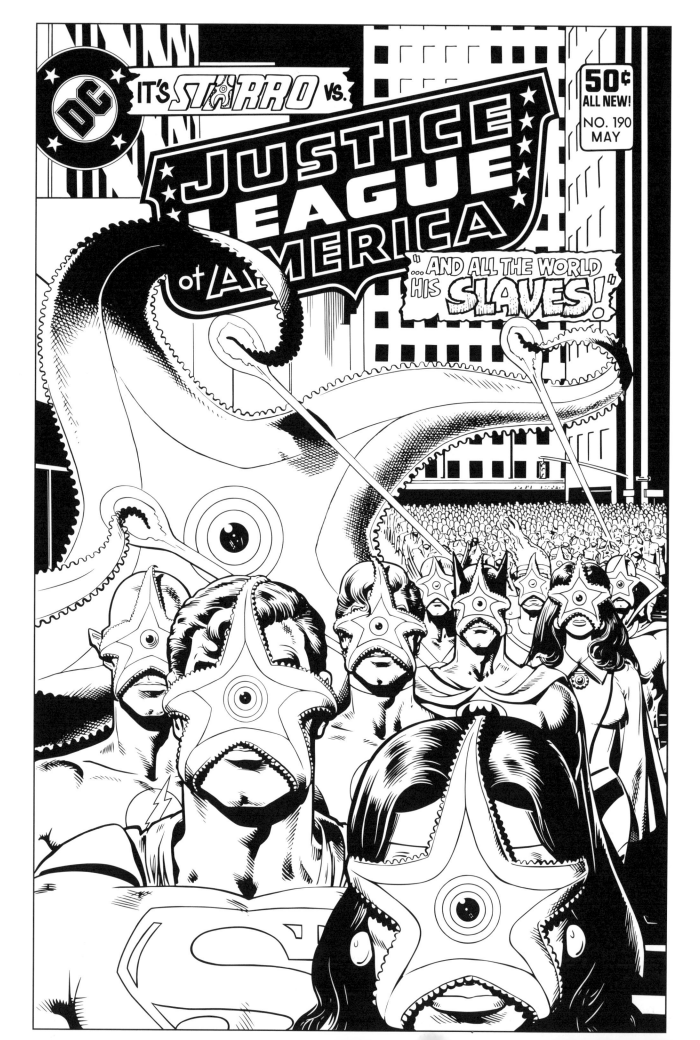

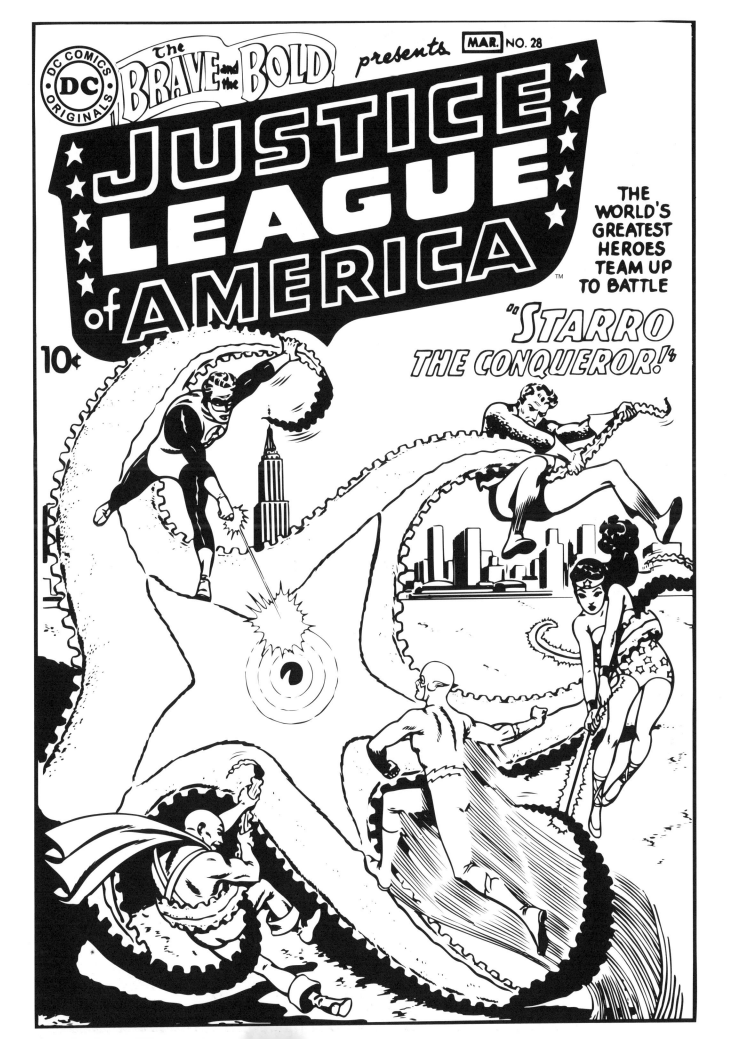

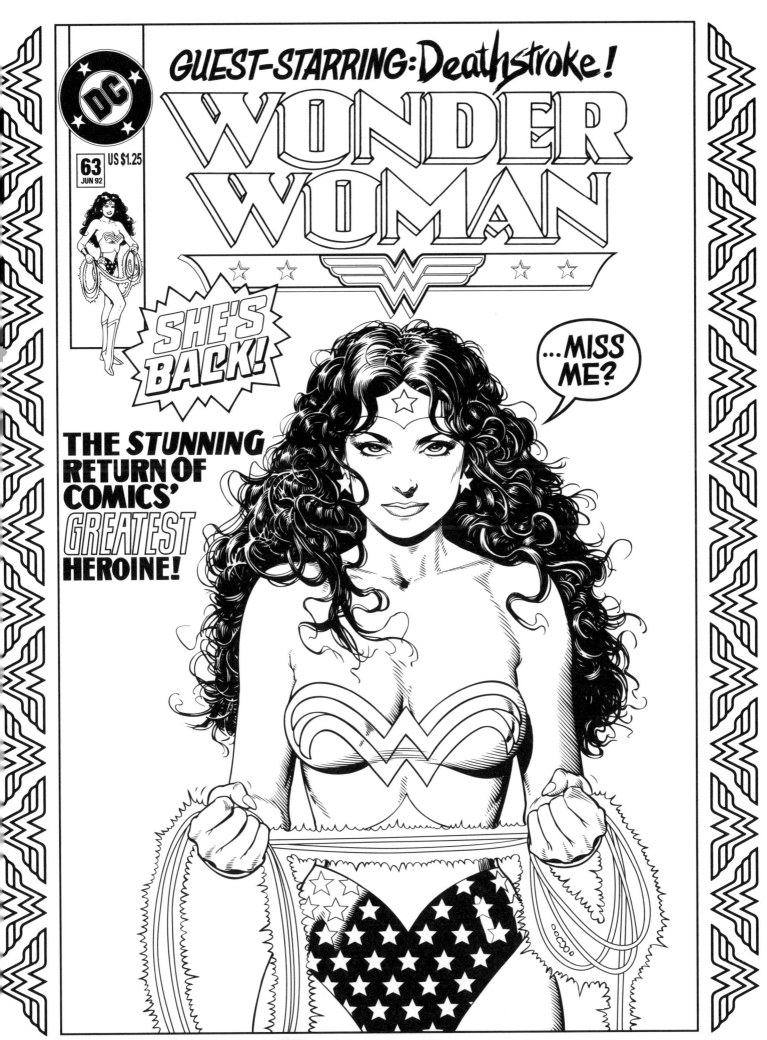

OCT.-NOV.
No.17

COMIC CAVALCADE

FIFTEEN CENTS

A GALAXY OF AMERICA'S GREATEST COMICS FEATURING Wonder Woman Green Lantern and The Flash!

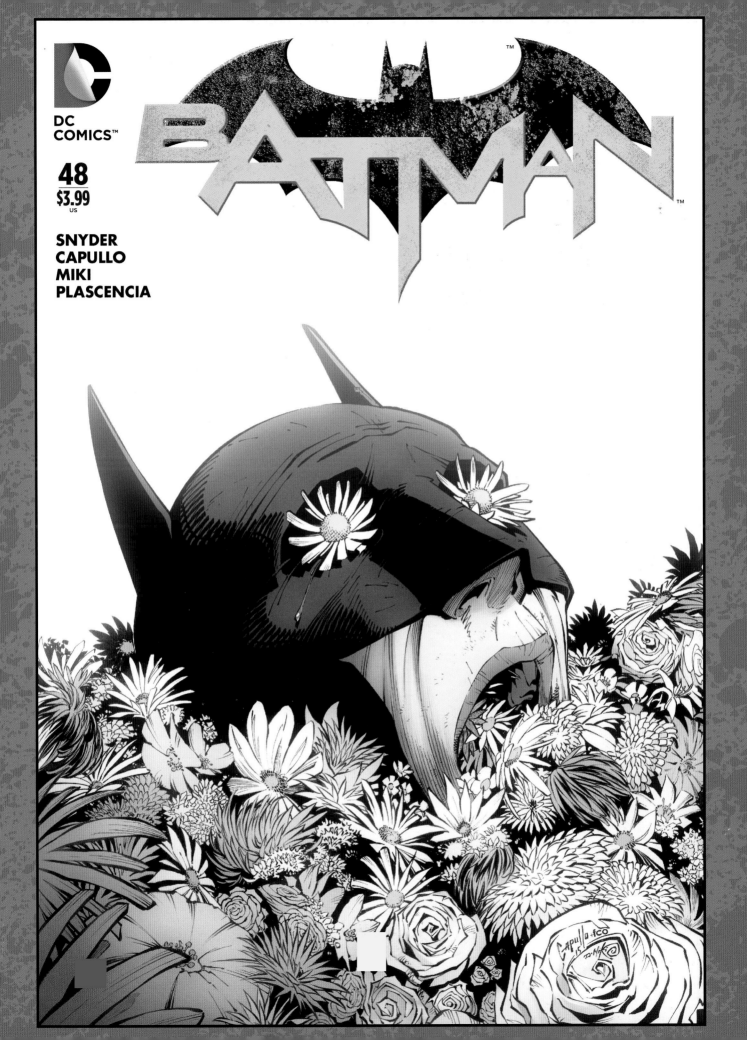

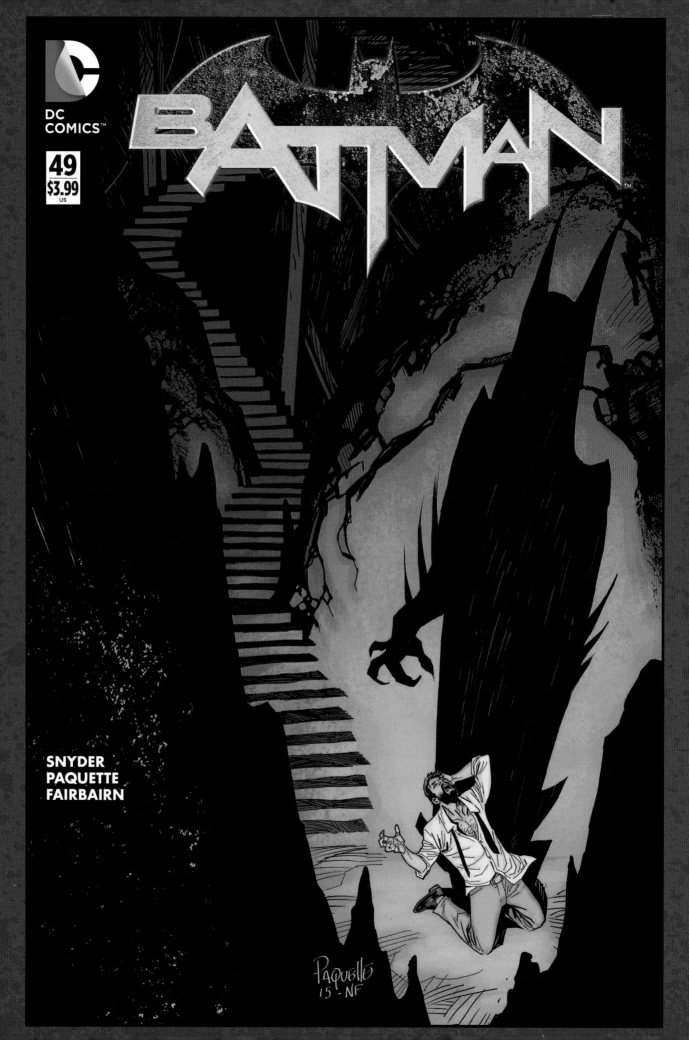

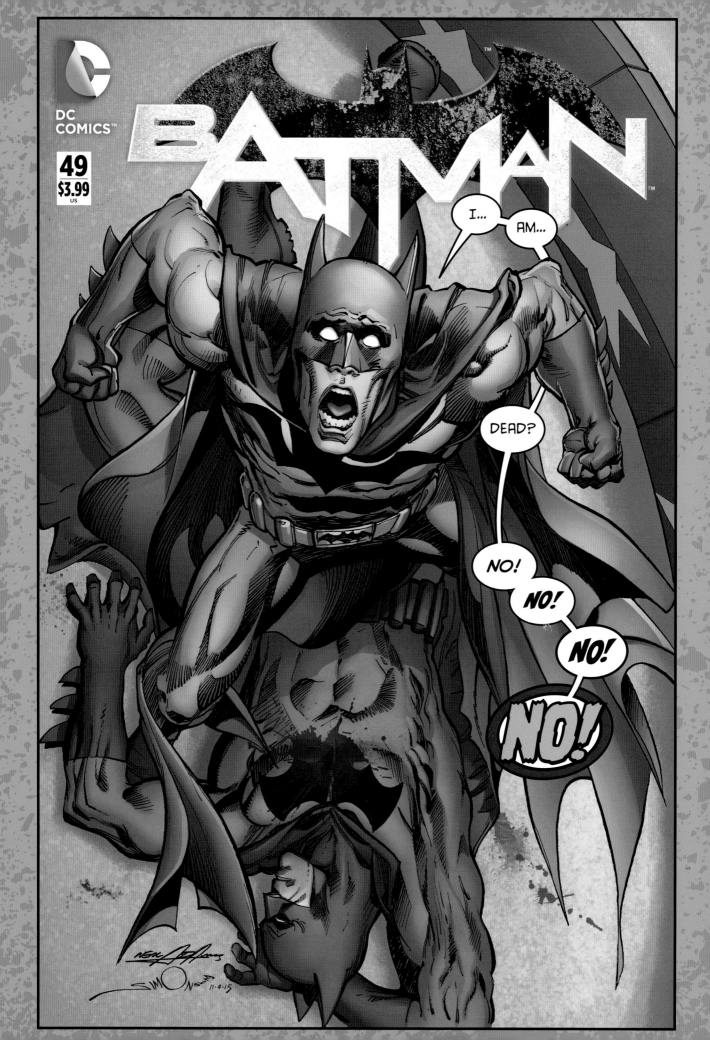

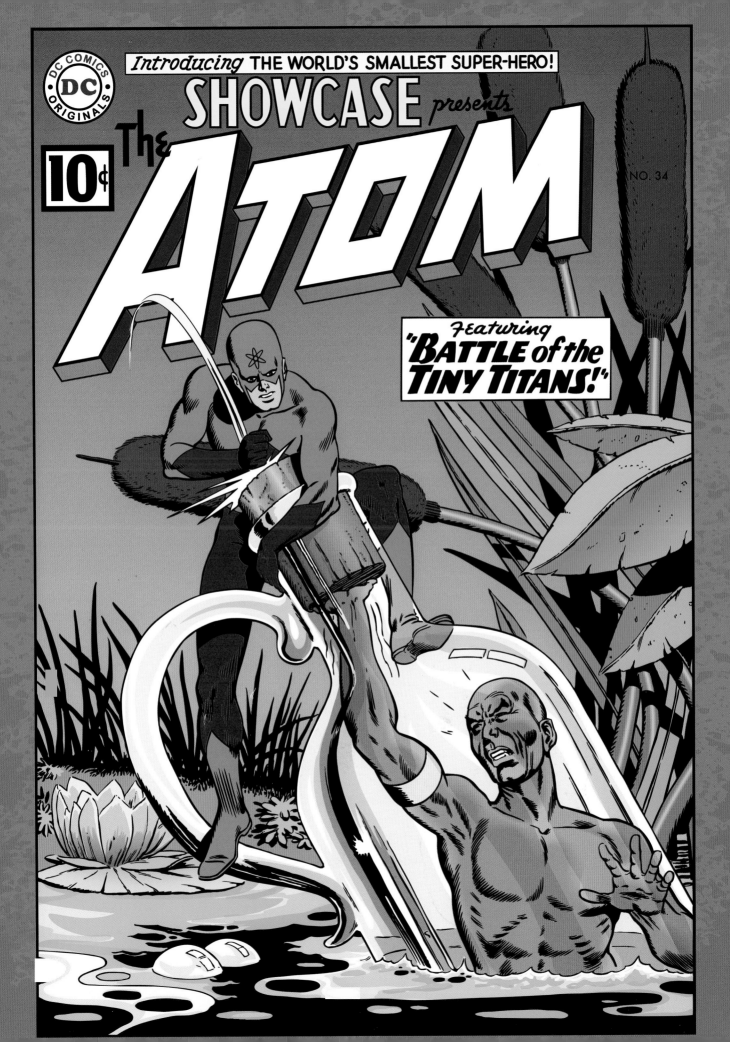

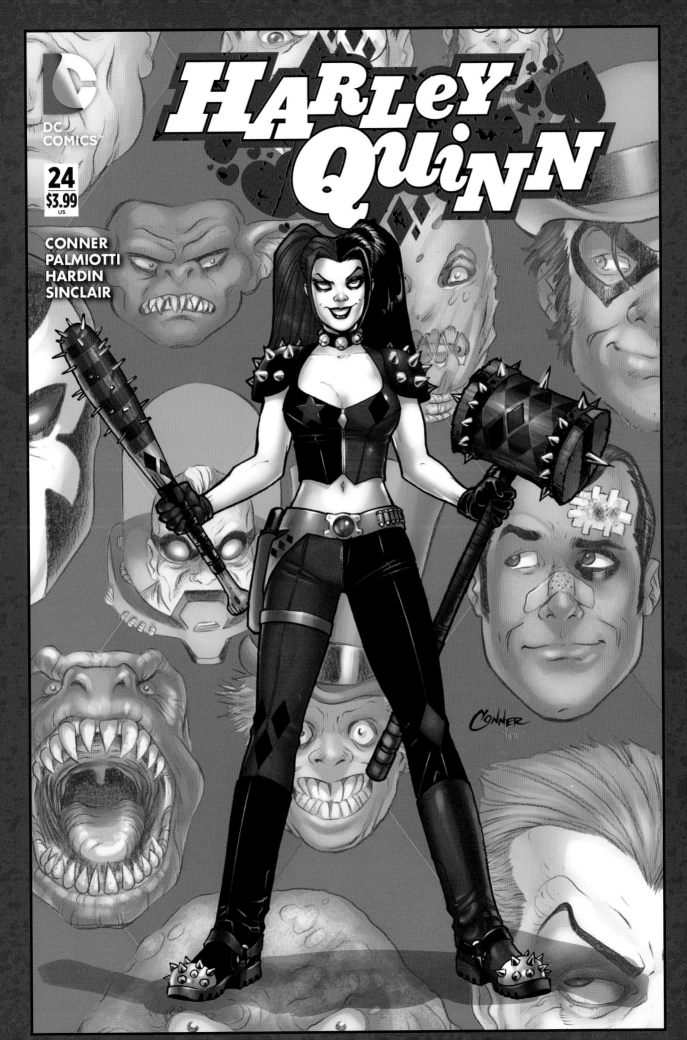

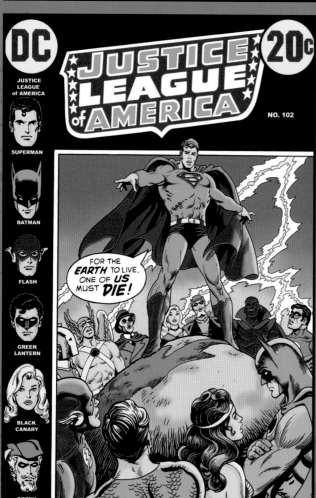

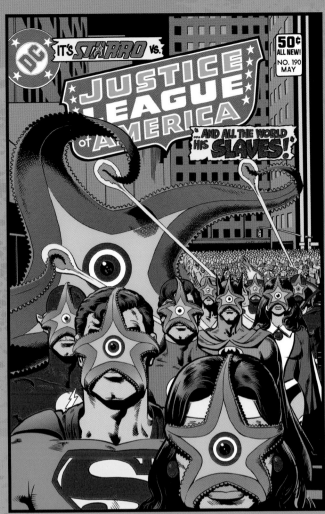

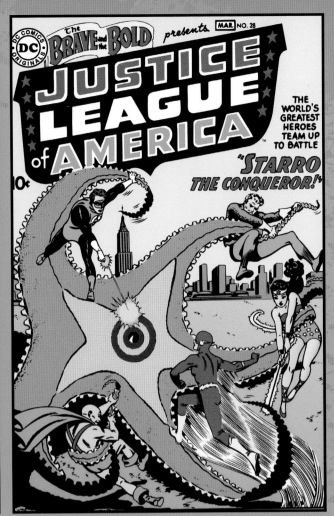

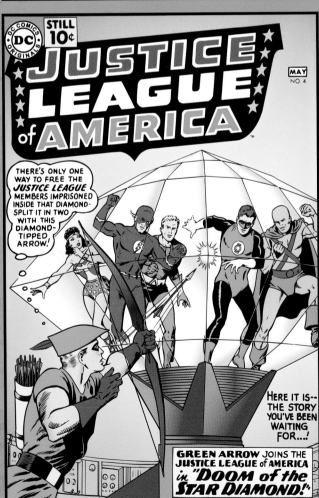

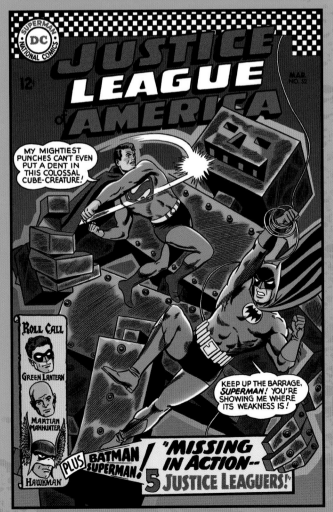

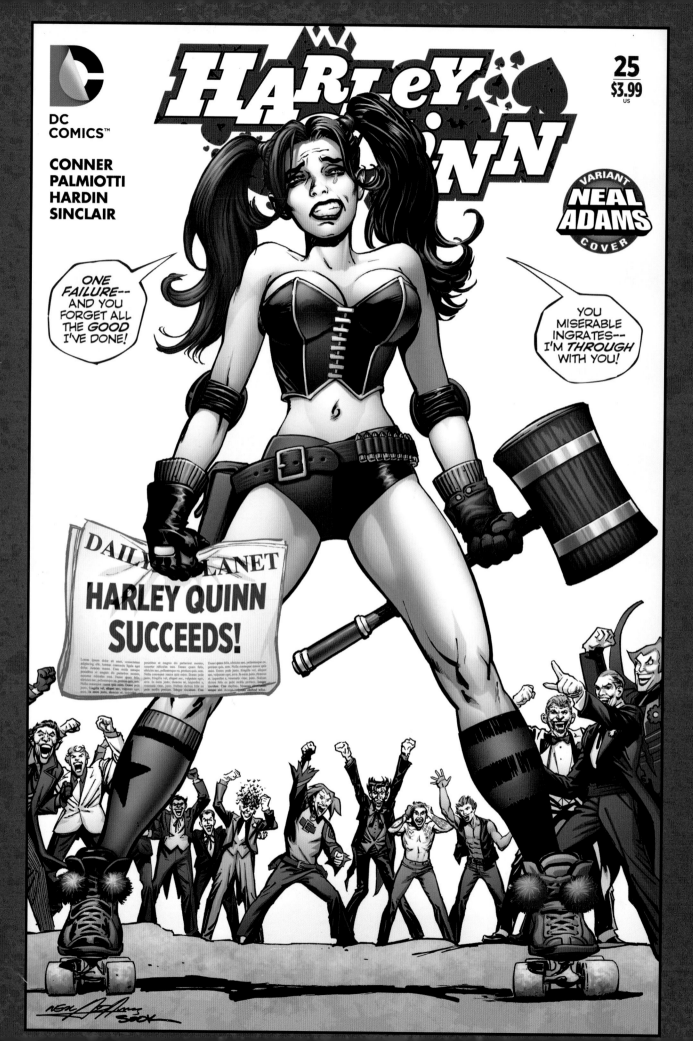

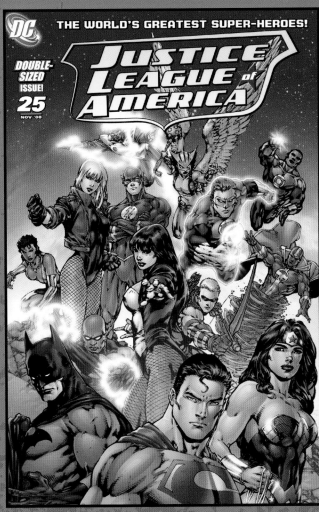

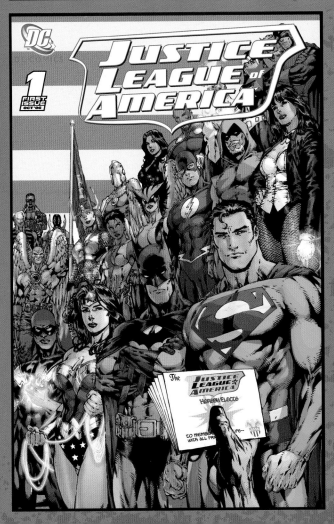

INSIGHT
EDITIONS

PO Box 3088
San Rafael, CA 94912
www.insighteditions.com

Published under license by Studio Press, an imprint of Templar Publishing,
part of the Bonnier Publishing Group.

ISBN: 978-1-78370-619-8

Publisher: Raoul Goff
Acquisitions Manager: Robbie Schmidt
Art Director: Chrissy Kwasnik
Designer: Malea Clark-Nicholson
Executive Editor: Vanessa Lopez
Project Editor: Kelly Reed
Production Editor: Elaine Ou
Associate Editor: Katie DeSandro
Production Managers: Alix Nicholaeff, Thomas Chung, and Lina sp Temena
Production Coordinator: Leeana Diaz

ROOTS of PEACE REPLANTED PAPER

Insight Editions, in association with Roots of Peace, will plant two trees
for each tree used in the manufacturing of this book. Roots of Peace is an
internationally renowned humanitarian organization dedicated to eradicating
land mines worldwide and converting war-torn lands into productive farms
and wildlife habitats. Roots of Peace will plant two million fruit and nut
trees in Afghanistan and provide farmers there with the skills and support
necessary for sustainable land use.

Manufactured in Italy by Insight Editions

10 9 8 7 6 5 4 3 2 1